LABORATORY
EMBRYOLOGY
OF THE
FROG

LABORATORY EMBRYOLOGY OF THE FROG

LLOYD E. DOWNS

La Sierra College, La Sierra, California

WM. C. BROWN COMPANY PUBLISHERS

Dubuque, Iowa

Preface

This laboratory guide to the study of frog embryology follows the same plan as the author's *Laboratory Embryology of the Chick* published a few years ago. It is designed to give a thorough coverage of the development of the frog through the ten millimeter stage. If a less-thorough coverage is desired, some of the exercises may be omitted at the discretion of the instructor.

The illustrations in this manual are designed to help the student identify the various embryonic structures and also to help him visualize the embryos in the three dimensions. The conscientious student should find these illustrations very helpful. The superficial student should be warned against using them as a means of avoiding a careful and thorough study of the embryos themselves.

The illustrations were drawn by Mrs. Ione Brunt under the supervision of the author.

It is hoped that teachers of embryology will find this manual helpful in the laboratory study of the embryology of the frog.

Contents

List of Figures

Introduction

Materials Required

Each student should provide himself with the following materials:

1. Biology drawing paper, 8½ by 11.
2. Folder for drawings.
3. Set of colored pencils, plus hard and soft lead pencils.
4. Six inch ruler or straight edge.
5. Art blenders (French paper tortillion stomps).

Laboratory Procedure

Objectives:

1. To give meaning to the new embryological terms and concepts which the student encounters in his reading and in the classroom by providing him an opportunity to study actual embryos as whole mounts and in serial sections.
2. To give training in the techniques of the laboratory study of biological specimens, especially those where the use of the microscope is necessary.
3. To aid the student in visualizing the development of the frog as a continuous process and to help him integrate his studies and observations into a total picture.
4. To provide the student with the opportunity to learn the details of the structure and developmental processes of frog embryos.

Achievement of the Objectives:

The achievement of these objectives will depend to a great extent on the attitude and seriousness of purpose of the student himself. The student should seriously and thoughtfully engage in each exercise with these objectives in mind. The assigned work should not be considered simply a task to be done as quickly as possible, but rather as a means of achieving objectives. In addition to doing the assigned work the student should spend much time studying his sections and whole mounts and attempting to correlate them into a total developmental picture.

Drawings

Objectives:

1. To develop in the student the ability to observe accurately and in detail.
2. To aid in the learning process.
3. To give instruction in the making of scientific drawings.

Achievement of the Objectives:

In order that these objectives may be achieved the student should do all his drawings in the laboratory where the materials are available. He should base his drawings *exclusively* on his observations of embryos under the microscope and *never* on any visual aids that may be available. Models, charts and pictures in books, including the illustrations in this manual and so forth, are to be used *only* to help identify and study relationships. They are *never* to be used instead of the actual embryos in the making of drawings.

Drawings should be neat and accurate. Care should be taken to draw the parts in correct proportion. Artistic effects are unnecessary.

Your name and the date should be printed *in ink* in the upper right-hand corner of each sheet of drawing paper.

All labels should be printed horizontally and should be underlined. Lines connecting labels with the structures named should *never* cross each other. Plan your drawings so you provide ample room for labeling and so the page will look well balanced. Drawings should be large and generally not more than two on a page—for larger embryos only one. *Consult* your *instructor* about details before beginning any series of drawings.

Each drawing should be labeled fully. In drawings of sections where more than one drawing is on a page, the first drawing on *each* page should be fully labeled, but subsequent ones on that page should have labeled only those structures not found in the first drawing.

Whole mount drawings will be made with blenders. Cross-section drawings will be made with colored pencils. The colors represent the different membranes or basic parts of the embryo as follows:

Blue .... ectoderm
Red .... mesoderm
Yellow .... entoderm
Green .... nervous tissue
Brown .... notochord

EXERCISE I

The Frog Embroyo:
The Zygote and Cleavage Stages

Material

Microscope slides of the frog egg and early and late cleavage stages including whole mounts and serial sections.

Discussion

The Egg:

The frog egg (*Rana pipiens*) is moderately telolecithal, with the more active cytoplasm concentrated toward the animal pole and the yolk material concentrated toward the vegetal pole.

When released from the ovary, the egg is about 1.7 mm to 2.0 mm in diameter. It is surrounded by a delicate *vitelline membrane* and an outer tougher membrane called the *chorion*. The animal hemisphere of the egg is black because of an accumulation of black pigment granules in the peripheral oöplasm, but the vegetal hemisphere remains creamy white. As they descend the oviduct, the eggs are covered by three distinct layers of gelatinous material.

After being extruded into the water, the eggs are fertilized and the gelatinous layers absorb water and swell, forming the three jelly membranes. Usually the sperm enters the pigmented half of the egg at some point about 40° from the animal pole. As soon as the egg is fertilized, water escapes from it into the space between it and the chorion. This accumulation of water releases the egg from the chorion so that it floats free. Since the vegetal pole of the egg is heavier, it floats with the pigmented animal hemisphere up.

After sperm entrance, the peripheral oöplasm flows toward the point of entrance. The flow is especially strong at a point in the animal hemisphere opposite the point of entrance. The flow of oöplasm carries pigment granules with it, which results in a thinning of pigmentation in the area most affected by the flow. This results in a crescent-shaped area of reduced pigmentation called the *grey crescent*.

Cleavage:

Shortly after fertilization the egg, which is now called a *zygote*, undergoes a series of rapid mitotic divisions. Since a period of growth does not intervene between successive divisions, the resulting *blastomeres* become smaller and smaller. For this reason this type of cell division is called *cleavage*. The first cleavage begins at the animal pole and progresses toward the vegetal pole, dividing the zygote completely into two equal *blastomeres*. The second cleavage also starts at the animal pole and is at right angles to the first, resulting in four equal blastomeres. This type of cleavage is total and equal and is called *holoblastic cleavage*. The third cleavage is at right angles to the other two but is located somewhat above the equator of the egg, resulting in four smaller blastomeres near the animal pole called *micromeres* and four larger ones composing the rest of the embryo called *macromeres*. Subsequent cleavages occur more rapidly among the micromeres than among the macromeres with the result that the former become much more numerous than the latter. The sluggish cleavage rate of the macromeres is probably due to their yolk content; they are called *yolk cells*. Eventually, they will be broken down to provide food for the embryo.

Exercise

With the microscope, study your whole mounts and early and late cleavage serials thoroughly. Compare the serials with the whole mounts until you can visualize the progress of cleavage in three dimensions. Continue your study until you have mastered this point.

Drawings

Make all drawings *directly* from the specimens. *Never* copy from other drawings. Make a drawing of a frog's egg with its jelly coats. Make a series of six whole mount drawings showing the zygote and the first five cleavages. Omit the jelly coats. Draw a hemisection of a zygote in early cleavage and another one in late cleavage.

Labels

Label the following structures on your drawings:

Animal Hemisphere	Micromeres
Blastomeres	Segmentation Cavity
Chorion	Vegetal Hemisphere
Jelly Membranes	Vitelline Membrane
Macromeres	

Questions

1. What is the function of the jelly membranes?
2. What is the adaptive value of having the pigmented hemisphere of the egg facing upward?
3. What two adaptations contribute to keeping the pigmented hemisphere of the egg upward?
4. What is the function of the yolk in telolecithal eggs?
5. What is the effect of the yolk on cleavage?
6. Give three results of fertilization.
7. Give the fate of the macromeres.
8. How is cleavage different from ordinary cell division?
9. How does the frog zygote compare in size with adult frog cells?
10. Considering the answer to question 9, what might be one function of cleavage?

The Frog Embroyo:
Blastula, Gastrulation and Gastrula

Material

Microscope slides of whole mounts and serial sections of frog blastula, early gastrula and late gastrula.

Discussion

The Blastula:

Beginning at about the eight blastomere stage, a cavity appears among the blastomeres. This is called the *segmentation cavity*. As cleavages continue, a blastula is gradually formed. The segmentation cavity is now called the *blastocoel*. It lies near the animal pole. In the early blastula the floor of the blastocoel consists of macromeres, while its roof consists of several layers of micromeres. In a fully developed blastula the micromeres of the animal hemisphere extend down below the equator. In other words, they have partly overgrown the larger yolk cells. The micromeres in the equatorial region seem to be dividing rapidly and are called the *germ ring*.

Gastrulation:

The cells of the germ ring continue to overgrow the yolk cells, advancing over them from all directions. When these cells reach a point in the area of the grey crescent which is about halfway between the equator and the vegetal pole, a small transverse notch appears, at which point the micromeres turn inward. This notch is the *dorsal lip of the blastopore*. In other areas the micromeres continue their overgrowth of the yolk cells. As time passes, the blastopore becomes crescent shaped and then ring shaped. When the blastopore is completed, it is filled with a mass of yolk cells known as the *yolk plug*.

Involution begins with the cells just above the dorsal lip of the blastopore. These cells turn inward instead of continuing their progress toward the vegetal pole. The other cells of the germ ring continue their movement toward the vegetal pole, but as the vegetal hemisphere becomes completely overgrown by the micromeres, the latter converge on the blastopore with the resulting completion of this structure. What began as an inward migration of a few cells just above the blastopore becomes, as the blastopore is completed, a massive migration of micromeres over the surface of the embryo toward the blastopore. As these cells reach the blastopore, they tumble over the edge and assume positions on the inside, forming the roof of the *gastrocoel* or *archenteron*. The cells of the roof of the archenteron are called *mesentoderm*, except in the middorsal region where they make up the *chordamesoderm*.

Exercise

Review thoroughly the slides of Exercise I and then study the whole mounts and serials of the blastula until you can visualize clearly the completed blastula in three dimensions and until you can trace in your mind the course of events which lead from the zygote to the completed blastula. Use available visual aids.

Having mastered the blastula and its formation, study the whole mounts and serials of early and late gastrulae. Study these slides and the visual aids available until you have complete mastery of the process of gastrulation and the structure of the completed gastrula.

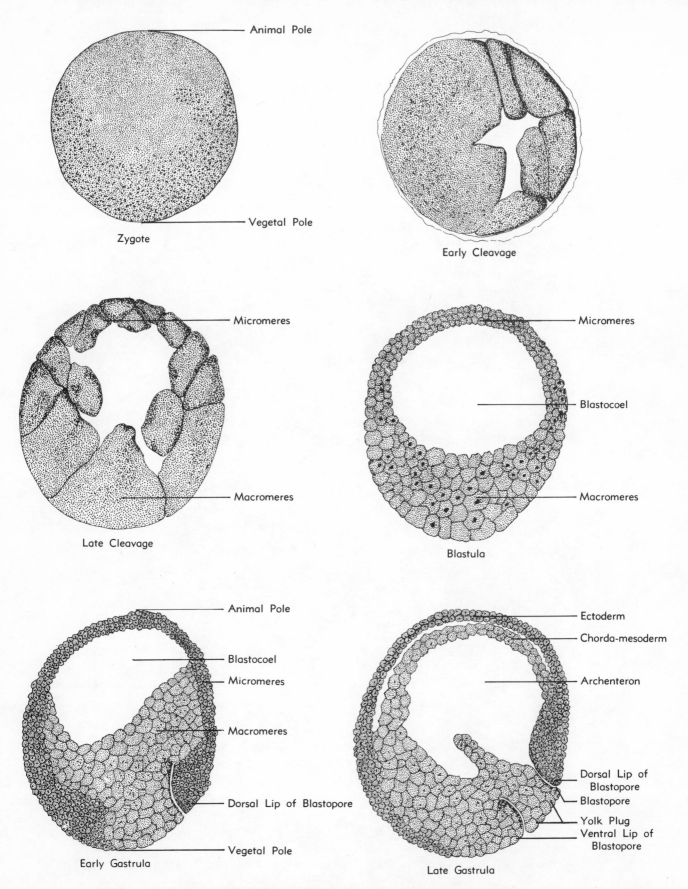

Figure 1. Frog Development, Early Stages: Cleavage, Blastula
and Gastrula.

6

Drawings

Draw the following in median sagittal sections:

1. A fully developed blastula.
2. An early gastrula.
3. A late gastrula.

Be sure to make all drawings from your slides *only*.

Labels

Label the following structures on your drawings:

Archenteron	Germ Ring
Blastocoel	Macromeres
Blastopore	Mesentoderm
Chordamesoderm	Micromeres
Dorsal Lip of Blastopore	Yolk Plug
Ectoderm	

Questions

1. Describe a frog blastula and explain the relationship between its parts.
2. Explain clearly the process of gastrulation in the frog.
3. Look up gastrulation in books on experimental embryology and explain what is accomplished by gastrulation.
4. What is the difference between chordamesoderm and mesentoderm?
5. What happens to the blastocoel during gastrulation?
6. Define epiboly, involution, archenteron.
7. Compare gastrulation in the frog with the same process in amphioxus.
8. Give reasons for the differences between gastrulation in the frog and in amphioxus.

The Frog Embroyo: Nerulation and the Nerula

Material

Whole mounts and serial sections of frog embryos in the neural plate, neural fold and neural tube stages.

Discussion

The completed gastrula consists of two layers, each several cells thick. The outer one is the *ectoderm* and the inner one is the *mesentoderm*, including the *chordamesoderm*. During nerulation, changes occur in both of these layers.

The mesentoderm delaminates into *mesoderm* and *entoderm*. The chordamesoderm occupies a position in the middorsal line. It separates from the mesoderm laterally and later from the entoderm ventrally and becomes the notochord. The dorsal portion of the mesoderm on either side of the notochord thickens and constitutes the *dorsal,* or *segmental mesoderm.* The rest of the mesoderm is called the *lateral mesoderm.* It splits into two layers. The outer one is the *somatic mesoderm,* and the inner one is the *splanchnic mesoderm.* As yet a *coelom* is not present, but it will later develop as a cavity between the somatic and the splanchnic mesoderm. The somatic and the splanchnic mesodermal layers and the entoderm grow ventrally between the ectoderm and the yolk cells, and the respective layers finally fuse with each other in the midventral line. This leaves the yolk cells within the completed gut, and the somatic and splanchnic mesodermal layers and the coelom become continuous from one side to the other.

The ectoderm consists of two parts. The outer one is an epithelium one cell thick and the inner one is several cells thick. Above the notochord a wide strip of the inner layer of ectoderm thickens and flattens forming the *neural plate.* The right and left borders of the neural plate become elevated and curve inward forming the *neural folds.* The neural folds converge toward the middorsal line and fuse together forming the *neural tube.* The superficial ectoderm becomes continuous over the neural tube. Laterally, on either side of the neural tube and between it and the superficial ectoderm are two thick bands of cells called the *neural crest.*

Before the fusion of the anterior neural folds, the deeper layer of ectoderm anterio-lateral to them becomes thickened, forming the *sense plates.* Behind these the *gill plates,* another pair of thickenings, form. From the sense plates will come the mandibular arches, the olfactory placodes, the oral suckers, the lenses of the eyes and the fifth and seventh cranial ganglia. The paired visceral arches, except for the mandibular, arise from the gill plates.

Exercise

Study your whole mounts and your serial sections of the neural plate, neural fold and neural tube stages until you can visualize clearly in three dimensions the structure of the completed nerula and also the developmental events leading up to it. Review Exercise 1 and 2 and correlate them with this exercise into a total developmental picture up to this stage. Keep at this study until you master it and do *not* proceed to your drawings until you have.

8

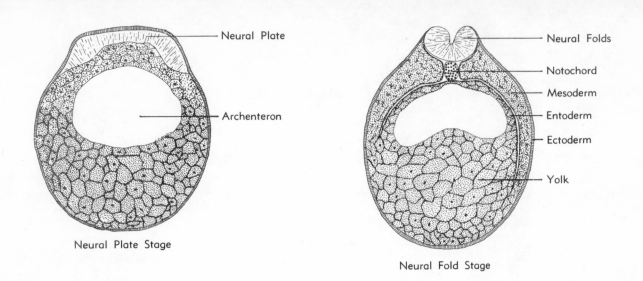

Neural Plate

Archenteron

Neural Plate Stage

Neural Folds

Notochord

Mesoderm

Entoderm

Ectoderm

Yolk

Neural Fold Stage

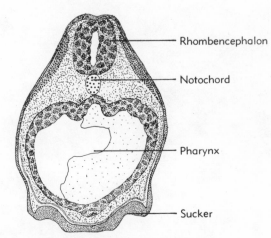

Mesencephalon

Prosencephalon

Optic Lobe

Olfactory Placode

Hypophysis

Neural Tube Stage Section Through the Brain

Rhombencephalon

Notochord

Pharynx

Sucker

Neural Tube Stage Section Through the Pharynx

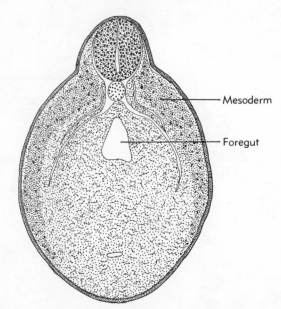

Mesoderm

Foregut

Neural Tube Stage Section Through the Foregut

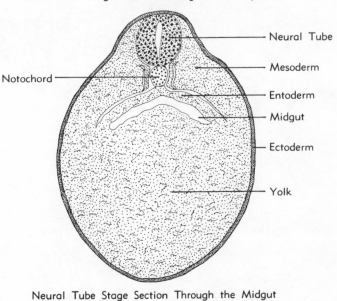

Neural Tube

Mesoderm

Entoderm

Midgut

Ectoderm

Yolk

Notochord

Neural Tube Stage Section Through the Midgut

Figure 2. Frog Development: Neural Plate, Neural Groove and
Neural Tube Stages.

9

Drawings

Make the following drawings:

1. Whole mounts of neural plate, neural fold and neural tube embryos.
2. Three cross sections of the neural plate stage:
   a. Through the head region.
   b. Through the midbody region.
   c. Through the posterior region.
3. One representative cross section through the neural fold stage.
4. Three cross sections through the neural tube stage:
   a. Through the optic lobes.
   b. Through the liver diverticulum.
   c. Through the hindgut.

Labels

Label the following structures on your drawings:

Archenteron	Entoderm
Coelom	Gill Plate
Dorsal Mesoderm	Hindgut
Ectoderm	Lateral Mesoderm
Liver Diverticulum	Olfactory Pits
Neural Crest	Optic Lobe
Neural Folds	Sense Plate
Neural Plate	Somatic Mesoderm
Neural Tube	Splanchnic Mesoderm
Notochord	Yolk Cells

Questions

1. Compare the differentiation of mesoderm and entoderm from each other in amphioxus and the frog.
2. Trace the development of the neural tube.
3. Trace the development of the notochord.
4. Where were the cells that were to become notochord located at the beginning of gastrulation?
5. Trace the development of the neural crest.
6. Describe the development of the optic lobes.
7. In what tissue do the olfactory pits form?
8. Trace the relationship between the yolk cells and the archenteron.
9. In what tissue does the neural tube form?
10. Where does the neural plate form in relation to the notochord?

EXERCISE IV

The Four Millimeter Frog Embryo
Whole Mount

Material

A whole mount of a 4 mm frog embryo.

Discussion

The division of the embryonic development of any animal into stages is, of course, arbitrary and artificial. Development progresses smoothly without reference to these man-made stages. The stages, however, are useful as learning and teaching devices.

In order to understand the 4 mm embryo, it is necessary to go back to the nerula and trace the changes which have occurred.

During gastrulation the embryo elongates along its anterio-posterior axis, becoming oval in shape. After gastrulation, it continues to elongate, and by the time it is 4 mm in length, it has developed a *tail bud* and a differentiated *head region*.

The neural folds join together to form a completed *neural tube*, first in the hindbrain region. From here, closure of the neural groove progresses in both directions. Openings at the anterior end and at the posterior end persist for a time and are called the *anterior* and the *posterior neuropores*, respectively.

The anterior end of the neural tube enlarges and bends ventrally over the end of the notochord. This is called the *ventral* flexure. This enlarged portion of the neural tube differentiates into the three primary brain vesicles. Beginning with the most anterior they are the *prosencephalon*, the *mesencephalon* and the *rhombencephalon*. The prosencephalon dilates laterally to form the *optic vesicles*, ventrally to form the *infundibulum* and dorsally to form the *epiphysis*. The notochord

lies ventral to the neural tube and dorsal to the gut. It is composed of what appear to be vacuolated cells. The cells of the neural tube adjacent to the end of the notochord thicken and form the *tuberculum posterius*. Lateral to the rhombencephalon are the auditory vesicles. These were formed by invaginations of ectoderm.

The mass of yolk cells still is a prominent feature of the embryo. The *gut* lies dorsal and anterior to this mass. Dorsal to the yolk the gut is narrow, but anterior to the yolk it is considerably expanded. Anterio-medially the ectoderm invaginates, forming the *stomodaeum*. An evagination of the foregut pushes out to meet the stomodaeum. The stomodaeum will become the mouth. Where the ectoderm of the stomodaeum makes contact with the entodermal evagination, a thin membrane persists for a time. This is the *oral plate*. A bud of the stomodael ectoderm pushes upward toward the brain and forms the *hypophysis*. A ventral diverticulum pushes ventrad and caudad from the foregut into the mass of yolk cells. This is the liver diverticulum. At the caudal end of the embryo another ectodermal invagination, the *protodaeum*, makes contact with the hindgut. Here the separating membrane is called the *anal plate*. Three or four lateral evaginations of the entoderm of the pharynx may be observed. These are the *pharyngeal* or *visceral pouches*. These push outward and are met by *ectodermal furrows*. By means of these pouches and furrows the *visceral arches* are differentiated in the gill plate.

In the 4 mm embryo the dorsal mesoderm has differentiated into twelve or more pairs of mesodermal *somites*. In the anterior portion of the embryo, the intermediate mesoderm has differ-

entiated into *nephrotomes*. The lateral mesoderm is composed of two layers, the *somatic mesoderm* and the *splanchnic mesoderm*. There is as yet no *coelom* between these two mesodermal layers, except under the foregut where the *pericardial cavity* is forming.

The *heart* at this stage is represented by a pair of troughs in the splanchnic mesoderm beneath the pharynx. In the space between these troughs and the entoderm of the pharynx some mesenchyme cells can be observed. These mesenchyme cells will form the *endocardium* and the troughs will fuse and form the *epimyocardium*.

Exercise

Place the slide of your 4 mm whole mount on the microscope and study it thoroughly. Compare what you see with the available visual aids and identify all of the external structures you can see. The embryo has been cleared so some of the internal structures are also visible. Study and identify these.

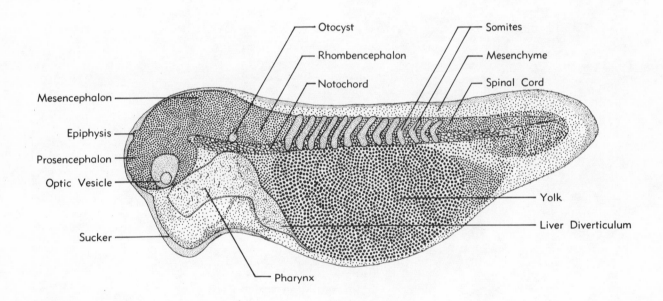

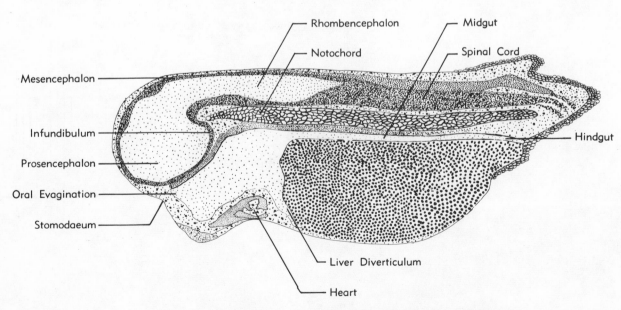

Figure 3.   Four Millimeter Frog Embryo Whole Mount (above) and Median Sagittal Section (below).

12

Drawing

Make an accurate drawing of *your* whole mount including all of the internal and external structures you can see. Turn the focusing knob on your microscope up and down to bring the different levels into focus.

Labels

Label the following structures on your drawing:

Auditory Vesicle	Pharynx
Epiphysis	Proctodaeum
Gut	Prosencephalon
Head	Rhombencephalon
Hypophysis	Somites
Infundibulum	Spinal Cord
Liver Diverticulum	Stomodaeum
Mesencephalon	Tail Bud
Neural Tube	Tuberculum Posterius
Notochord	Ventral Flexure
Optic Vesicle	Visceral Clefts
Oral Suckers	Yolk Cell Mass

Questions

1. Trace the steps in the development of the nervous system from the late gastrula stage to the 4 mm stage.
2. What structures form from sense plate material?
3. What relationship will develop between the infundibulum and the hypophysis?
4. Describe the origin of the auditory vesicles.
5. Where in the 4 mm embryo will the heart form?
6. Describe the extent to which heart development has occurred up to the 4 mm stage.
7. What is the position of the neural tube in relation to the notochord?
8. What is the position of the gut in relation to the notochord?
9. Describe the development of the liver up to this stage.
10. Describe the embryology of the mouth.

The Four Millimeter Frog Embryo
Cross Sections

Material

A serial cross-section slide of a 4 mm frog embryo.

Discussion

A serial cross section is prepared by cutting thin cross sections from an embryo in sequence beginning at the head end. These sections are spread in order on the slide.

As seen under the microscope, a whole mount is essentially a two-dimensional structure. Serial sections are designed to give you the third dimension. To learn what you should from serials, you must constantly compare each section studied with the whole mount and think of it in its proper place in the whole mount until you can visualize the embryo and all its structures in three dimensions.

Before beginning this exercise, very carefully study again the discussion in Exercise IV.

Exercise

Put your 4 mm serial cross-section slide on your microscope. Locate the most anterior sections and slowly and thoroughly study the sections in order from head to tail. Try to fix in your mind a picture of the different kinds of sections observed. Study the available visual aids, compare your sections to them and try to grasp the significance of what you have seen. Spend a considerable amount of time comparing your sections with the visual aids until you can visualize the embryo in three dimensions.

Put your 4 mm whole mount on the microscope again and try to interpret its observable features in terms of your new three-dimensional concept.

Keep at it until you can do this. Compare this embryo with the ones previously studied and continue your study until you can visualize all the changes that have occurred.

Drawings

Since the purpose of studying sections of embryos is to enable the student to visualize the embryo in three dimensions, the student should draw as many sections as are necessary both to accomplish this purpose and to illustrate *all* the structures of the embryo. Since embryos vary somewhat, the choice of sections to draw must, to some extent, be left to the student; however, the following suggestive list may help. Use color code.

1. Section through the epiphysis.
2. Section through the optic lobes.
3. Section through the infundibulum.
4. Section through auditory vesicles.
5. Section through the heart region.
6. Section through the liver diverticulum.
7. Section through the yolk mass.
8. Section through the proctodaeum.

Labels

Label the following structures on your drawings:

Auditory Vesicle	Mesencephalon
Endocardium	Mesenchyme
Epimyocardium	Midgut
Epiphysis	Notochord
Hindgut	Olfactory Pit
Hypophysis	Optic Lobes
Infundibulum	Pharynx
Liver Diverticulum	Proctodaeum

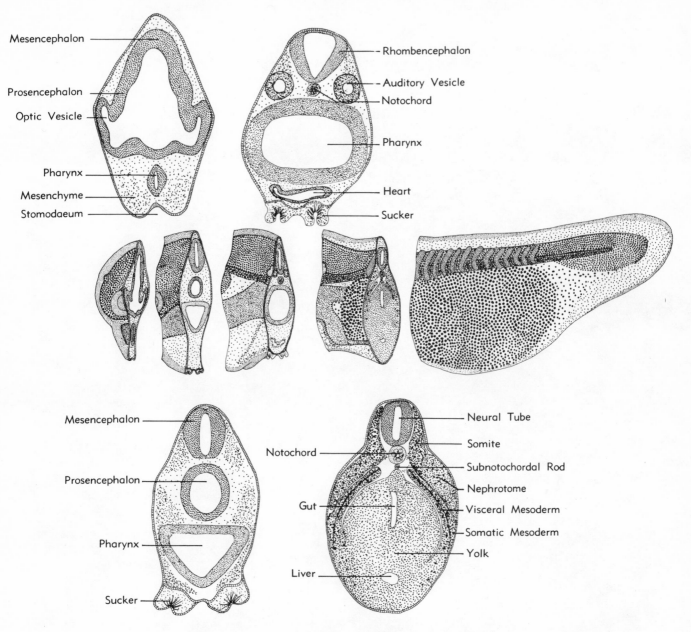

Figure 4. Four Millimeter Frog Embryo Sectioned.

Pronephros
Prosencephalon
Rhombencephalon
Somatic Mesoderm
Somites
Spinal Cord
Splanchnic
   Mesoderm

Stomodaeum
Tuberculum Posterius
Visceral Arches I,
   II, III & IV
Visceral Pouches I,
   II, III & IV
Yolk Mass

Questions

1. From which germ layer are the auditory vesicles derived?

2. What is the relation of the optic vesicles to the brain?
3. What is the function of the notochord?
4. Why is the coelom almost entirely absent in the 4 mm frog embryo?
5. What is the function of the oral suckers?
6. Into what two brain vesicles will the prosencephalon divide?
7. To which of the answers to Question 6 are the optic stalks attached?
8. The epiphysis and the infundibulum are evaginations of what brain vesicle?

15

EXERCISE VI

The Four Millimeter Frog Embryo
Sagittal and Frontal Sections

Material

Serial sagittal and frontal sections of a 4 mm frog embryo.

Discussion

Review again the discussions in Exercises IV and V. The study of the sagittal and frontal series will provide you with additional help in solving your problem of visualizing the 4 mm embryo in three dimensions.

Exercise

Put the serial sagittal section slide on your microscope and study the sections from side to side. In your mind try to locate each section where it belongs in the whole mount. Keep at it until you can do this. Look for the section that is nearest to being a median sagittal section. If you do not find a perfect median sagittal section on your slide, try to reconstruct one in your mind. By referring to visual aids identify all of the structures you observe in your median sagittal section. Note the digestive tract, its parts and its derivatives. Identify the *stomodaeum*, the *proctodaeum*, the yolk mass and the liver diverticulum. Examine the neural tube and locate the three brain vesicles. Note the structures that evaginate from the brain.

When you have mastered the serial sagittal sections, begin the study of the frontal series. Go through the series from the most dorsal section to the most ventral one. In your mind locate each section in the whole mount. Keep at it until

you can do this. Note those features that can be better understood by studying the frontal series, for instance, the visceral arches, than by studying the cross or sagittal sections.

Go back and review the three exercises on the 4 mm frog embryo until you have thoroughly mastered all the details of its anatomy. Having accomplished this, go back and trace from the zygote the development of all the various features of the 4 mm frog embryo. Be sure to master this before going on to more complex embryos.

Drawings

1. Draw a true median sagittal section of the 4 mm embryo. To do this you may have to combine observations from three or more sections.
2. Draw a frontal section showing the maximum length of the neural tube.
3. Draw one or two frontal sections as may be necessary to show the brain, optic vesicles, auditory vesicles and the notochord.
4. Draw a frontal section showing the visceral arches and pouches to the best advantage.
5. Draw a frontal section through the heart region.

Labels

Label the following structures each time they are found in the drawings above:

Auditory Vesicles	Hypophysis
Epiphysis	Infundibulum
Hindgut	Liver Diverticulum

Mesencephalon   Oral Evagination   Rhombencephalon   Visceral Arches I,
Mesenchyme   Pharynx   Spinal Cord   II, III & IV
Midgut   Proctodaeum   Stomodaeum   Visceral Pouches I,
Notochord   Prosencephalon   Tuberculum   II, III & IV
Optic Vesicles   Posterius   Yolk

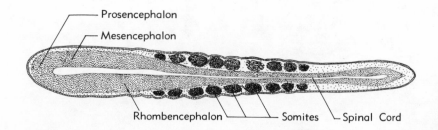

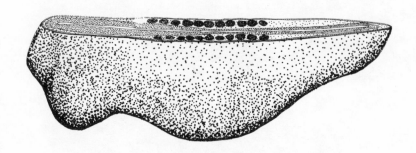

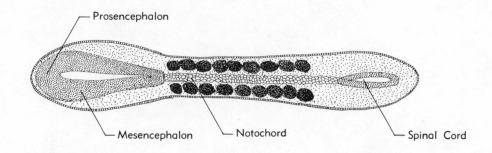

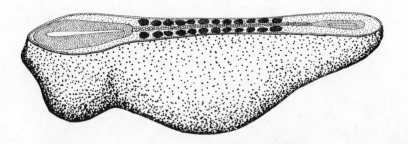

Figure 5. Four Millimeter Frog Embryo Frontal Sections.

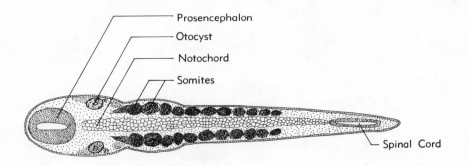

Prosencephalon

Otocyst

Notochord

Somites

Spinal Cord

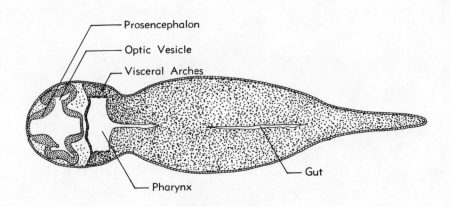

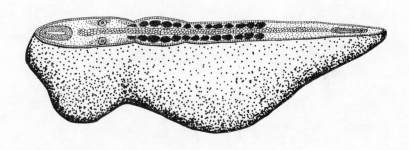

Prosencephalon

Optic Vesicle

Visceral Arches

Gut

Pharynx

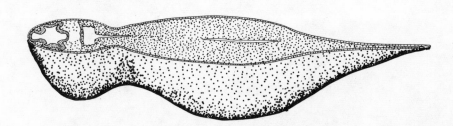

Figure 5. Four Millimeter Frog Embryo Frontal Sections, Continued.

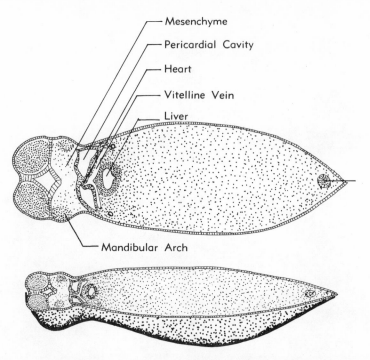

Figure 5.   Four Millimeter Frog Embryo Frontal Sections, Continued.

Questions

1. What features of the embryo are better understood by studying sagittal sections than by studying cross sections?
2. Frontal sections are better than cross or sagittal sections for the study of what features of the embryo?
3. How many visceral arches can you observe in your frontal series?
4. How many pharyngeal pouches can you observe in your frontal series?
5. What do you observe on either side of the notochord?
6. What do you observe to be the relationship between the optic vesicles and the brain?
7. Are the auditory vesicles related to the brain in the same way as the optic vesicles? If not, why not?
8. Describe the liver diverticulum.

The Six Millimeter Frog Embryo Whole Mount

Material

A whole mount slide of a 6 mm frog embryo.

Discussion

At 6 mm the embryo has developed into a larva and is ready to come out of the egg. It has developed definite body regions: head, body, tail. On the head are the *olfactory pits* and the *eyes*. Under the head are the *oral suckers* with which the larva will attach to objects. Laterally, on the posterior part of the head, are the *external gills*.

Some of the somites are beginning to differentiate into *dermatome, myotome* and *sclerotome*. The dermatomes will develop into the dermis of the skin. The myotomes will develop into the trunk musculature, and the sclerotomes will replace the notochord and develop into vertebrae.

In the midventral floor of the prosencephalon are two thickenings. One of these is the *optic chiasma* and posterior to it is the *torus transversus*. Between them is a depression, the *optic recess*. A line drawn from the optic recess to a point just anterior to the *epiphysis* divides the prosencephalon into the anterior *telencephalon* and the more posterior *diencephalon*. The *eyes, epiphysis* and the *infundibulum* are now parts of the diencephalon. Above the *infundibulum*, where the floor of the brain bends around the end of the notochord, is a slight thickening called the *posterior tubercle*. The *mesencephalon* remains undivided and the rhombencephalon will later differentiate into the *metencephalon* and *myelencephalon*. Posterior to the rhombencephalon is the *spinal cord*. On either side of the rhombencephalon are the *auditory vesicles,* and growing

under the forebrain medially in the region of the stomodaeum is the *hypophysis*.

The sense organs have undergone further development. The *lens* has formed from the ectoderm over the eye cups and has been incorporated into the eyes. At about this time the retina develops and the eyes become functional. The olfactory placodes have deepened and are now called *olfactory pits*. Also, at about this time a dorsal tubular projection called the *endolymphatic duct* grows out from each *auditory vesicle*. Just behind the eyes are the ganglia of the fifth cranial nerve, the *Gasserian ganglia*. Immediately anterior to the otocysts are the closely associated *ganglia* of the *seventh* and *eighth cranial nerves*. The *ganglia* of the *ninth* and *tenth cranial nerves* can be observed posterior to the auditory vesicles.

The *stomodaeum* is still a shallow depression, and the oral plate still separates it from the *oral evagination*. Ventrally on the pharynx is a depression which will become the *thyroid gland*, and farther back and also ventrally is the *liver diverticulum*.

In the lateral walls of the pharynx, paired entodermal pouches push out to meet paired ectodermal furrows which push in from the outside. The paired entodermal pouches are called *visceral pouches*. Eventually some of the pouches and furrows open to the outside, forming the *visceral clefts,* or *gill clefts*. The visceral pouches and their corresponding ectodermal furrows divide the lateral walls of the pharynx into paired thickenings called *visceral arches*. There will be a total of five pairs of visceral pouches and six pairs of visceral arches. *External gills* develop on the third, fourth and fifth visceral arches. The

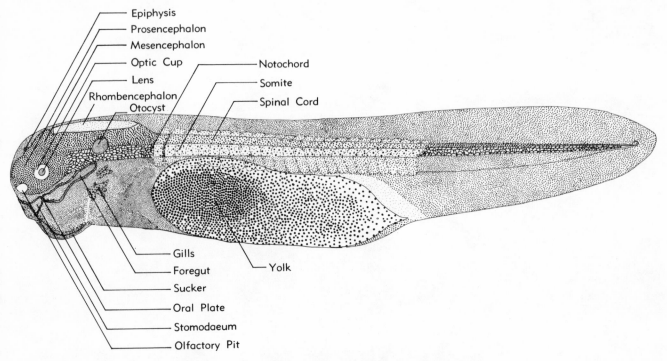

Figure 6.   Six Millimeter Frog Embryo Whole Mount.

midgut is a narrow tubular passage with a thin roof and a thick floor consisting of the mass of yolk cells. The midgut has no special differentiations. The *hindgut* together with the proctodaeum forms the cloaca. The anal plate has ruptured by this time.

Shortly before hatching (at about 6 mm) the blood vascular system of the embryo has been completed. It consists of a tubular heart which has coiled upon itself and differentiated into a *sinus venosus*, an *atrium*, a *ventricle* and a *truncus arteriosus*. The heart develops in a ventral cavity called the *pericardial cavity*. It lies on the ventral side of the body between the thyroid diverticulum and the liver diverticulum. The blood goes from the truncus arteriosus through the *afferent* and *efferent branchial arteries* to the *dorsal aortae*. These afferent and efferent branchial arteries form the *aortic arches* which pass through the visceral arches. From the dorsal aorta the blood is distributed to the body and to the vitelline blood vessels in the splanchnic mesoderm around the yolk. From the body the blood returns to the heart through the *anterior* and the *posterior cardinal veins*. On each side an anterior and a posterior cardinal vein join to form a common cardinal

vein, or *duct of Cuvier*. From the vitelline blood vessels around the yolk the blood returns to the heart through two vitelline veins.

Laterally and a little below the level of the notochord and just posterior to the heart region is the pronephric region. The *pronephros* consists of tubules and a duct. The *pronephric tubules* open into the coelom by means of a *nephrostome* and join the *pronephric duct* laterally. The pronephric duct empties into the gut in the region of the cloaca. Because of coiling, the pronephric tubules may be cut more than once in a given section.

Exercise

Place your slide of the 6 mm whole mount on your microscope and study its structure in detail. Compare with the visual aids available and identify what you see. Compare with your 4 mm embryo and take careful note of all of the changes that have occurred. Mentally trace from its beginning the development of each structure you see.

Drawing

Make a drawing of your 6 mm whole mount. Be sure to have the various parts in correct pro-

portion. Include any internal structures that you can see.

Labels

Label the following structures on your drawing:

Endolymphatic Duct	Oral Plate
Epiphysis	Oral Suckers
External Gills	Otocyst
Foregut	Prosencephalon
Lens	Rhombencephalon
Mesencephalon	Somites
Notochord	Spinal Cord
Olfactory Pit	Stomodaeum
Optic Cup	Yolk

Questions

1. Trace a red blood cell from the time it leaves the sinus venosus going via the tail until it returns to the sinus venosus. Name in order every structure it passes through.
2. Do as in Question 1 except have it pass through the vitelline circuit.
3. What is the approximate length of the frog larva when it hatches?
4. What is the difference between an embryo and a larva?
5. Why does a young larva not have gill slits?
6. Into what structures does a somite differentiate?
7. Into what does each of the differentiated structures of Question 6 develop?
8. From what embryonic tissue do the ganglia of the cranial nerves develop?
9. What prevents a newly hatched larva from feeding?
10. In what structures are the aortic arches found?

The Six Millimeter Frog Embryo Median Sagittal Section

Material

A serial sagittal section of a six millimeter frog embryo.

Discussion

Carefully read again the discussion of Exercise VII.

Exercise

Place your slide on the microscope and go through the sections from one side of the embryo to the other. Compare the sections to the whole mount and in your mind try to reconstruct the embryo in three dimensions, especially the internal structures. Using the available visual aids identify all the structures you see and determine the relationship of the various parts to each other and to the intact embryo.

Drawing

Select the section that comes the nearest to being a median sagittal section and draw it. Very few serials will be cut accurately enough to produce a perfect median sagittal section, therefore, you may have to make your drawing a composite of about three different drawings but make it a median sagittal section.

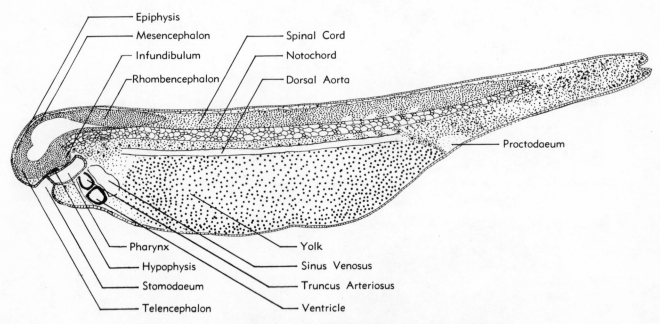

Figure 7. Six Millimeter Frog Embryo Median Sagittal Section.

23

Labels

Label the following structures on your drawing:

Dorsal Aorta	Rhombencephalon
Epiphysis	Sinus Venosus
Foregut	Spinal Cord
Hypophysis	Stomodaeum
Infundibulum	Telencephalon
Mesencephalon	Truncus Arteriosus
Notochord	Ventricle
Proctodaeum	Yolk

Questions

1. How would you draw a line that would correctly divide the prosencephalon into the telencephalon and the diencephalon?
2. Name the two thickenings on the floor of the prosencephalon.
3. From what germ layer is the hypophysis derived?
4. Describe the midgut.
5. From what is the cloaca formed?
6. Name the chambers of the heart.
7. Define the words afferent and efferent.
8. Name the cavity in which the heart lies.
9. What blood vessels carry the blood from the ventral aorta around the pharynx to the dorsal aorta?
10. From what germ layer is the thyroid gland derived?

EXERCISE IX

The Six Millimeter Frog Embryo
Serial Cross Sections

Material

A serial cross-section slide of a 6 mm frog embryo.

Discussion

Carefully review the discussions in Exercises V and VII. Study these until you understand clearly what you are to do and *why*.

Exercise

The "Exercise" portion of Exercise V should be carefully restudied before going further. Put your serial cross-section slide on the microscope and follow the directions of Exercise V carefully. Remember that an intelligent, conscientious approach to your laboratory exercises will pay big dividends.

Drawings

Read again the "Drawing" instructions of Exercise V. Note especially the reason given for the study of serial cross sections. This time no suggestive list of sections will be given. As you study the sections in order, you will find new structures appearing and the structural pattern changing. Each section that presents a new structure or a new structural pattern should be drawn. Because of its more advanced development, this embryo will require more drawings than the 4 mm did. Remember to make your drawings in good proportion and to use the color code.

Labels

Label the following structures on your drawings:

Afferent Branchial Artery
Anterior Cardinal Vein
Auditory Vesicle
Dermatome
Diencephalon
Dorsal Aorta
Foregut
Heart
Hypophysis
Lens
Mesencephalon
Mesenchyme
Midgut
Myotome
Notochord
Olfactory Pit
Optic Cup
Optic Stalk
Oral Sucker
Pharynx
Pronephric Duct
Pronephric Tubule
Prosencephalon
Rhombencephalon
Sclerotome
Somite
Spinal Cord
Stomodaeum
Subnotochordal Rod
Telencephalon
Thyroid
Truncus Arteriosus
Ventricle
Vitelline Blood Vessels
Yolk

Questions

1. From what germ layer are the auditory vesicles derived?
2. To which of the primary brain vesicles are the optic lobes attached?
3. To which of the secondary brain vesicles are the optic lobes attached?
4. List ten structural features of the six millimeter frog embryo which you have learned from the sagittal and cross sections and which you would not have learned from the whole mount.
5. Give the source of the neural crest cells.
6. Which two germ layers contribute to the oral plate?

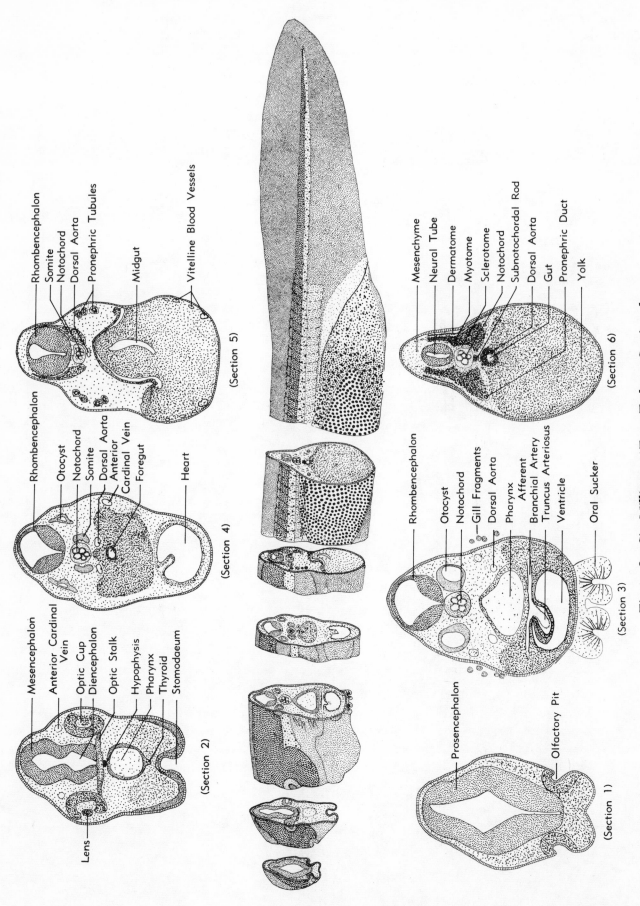

Mesencephalon
Anterior Cardinal Vein
Optic Cup
Diencephalon
Optic Stalk
Hypophysis
Pharynx
Thyroid
Stomodaeum

Lens

(Section 2)

Rhombencephalon
Otocyst
Notochord
Somite
Dorsal Aorta
Anterior Cardinal Vein
Foregut

Heart

(Section 4)

Rhombencephalon
Somite
Notochord
Dorsal Aorta
Pronephric Tubules

Midgut

Vitelline Blood Vessels

(Section 5)

Mesenchyme
Neural Tube
Dermatome
Myotome
Sclerotome
Notochord
Subnotochordal Rod
Dorsal Aorta
Gut
Pronephric Duct
Yolk

(Section 6)

Rhombencephalon
Otocyst
Notochord
Gill Fragments
Dorsal Aorta
Pharynx
Afferent Branchial Artery
Truncus Arteriosus
Ventricle

Oral Sucker

(Section 3)

Prosencephalon

Olfactory Pit

(Section 1)

Figure 8. Six Millimeter Frog Embryo Sectioned.

26

7. Name the two layers of the heart wall.
8. Name three outpocketings from the prosen-
    cephalon.
9. Name the chambers of the embryonic heart.
10. Why is it important to visualize an embryo
    in three dimensions?

EXERCISE X

The Six Millimeter Frog Embryo
Serial Frontal Sections

Material

A serial frontal section of a 6 mm frog embryo.

Discussion

The 6 mm embryo was discussed in detail in Exercise VII. Review that discussion before beginning this exercise.

Exercise

In this exercise follow the same procedures you used in the study of the frontal sections of the 4 mm embryo. Turn back to Exercise VI and study the directions again before continuing.

This is the last exercise on the 6 mm embryo. After completing this exercise, you should take each structure, organ and system of the 6 mm embryo and trace its development from the egg to its stage of development in the 6 mm embryo. Only by these repeated reviews of developmental processes can you master the subject of embryology.

Drawings

Beginning at the dorsal side draw a series of frontal sections that will illustrate the optimum detail of the organs and systems of the embryo. Use the guidelines given in Exercise IX to determine how many sections to draw.

Labels

Label the following structures on your drawings:

Aortic Arches
Auditory Vesicles
Coelom
Epiphysis
Gut
Hindgut
Lens
Liver
Mesencephalon
Neural Tube
Notochord
Olfactory Pit
Optic Cup
Oral Plate
Pericardial Cavity
Pharyngeal Pouches I & II
Pharynx
Pronephric Tubules
Prosencephalon
Rhombencephalon
Sinus Venosus
Somites
Stomodaeum
Truncus Arteriosus
Ventricle
Visceral Arches I, II, III & IV
Yolk

Questions

1. List all the things which you have learned about the 6 mm frog embryo that you would not have learned or would have found it more difficult to learn from the slides of the preceding three exercises.
2. What relationships are more easily observed in the frontal sections than in the cross sections?
3. What relationships are more easily observed in the frontal sections than in the sagittal sections?
4. What advantages as a learning tool do the cross sections have over the frontal sections?
5. How many pharyngeal pouches did you observe in your frontal sections?
6. What is the maximum number of pharyngeal pouches formed in the frog?

7. What develops from the first pharyngeal pouch?

8. How many visceral arches did you observe in your frontal sections?

9. What is the total number of visceral arches that will develop?

10. Explain any discrepancy between your answers to Questions 8 and 9.

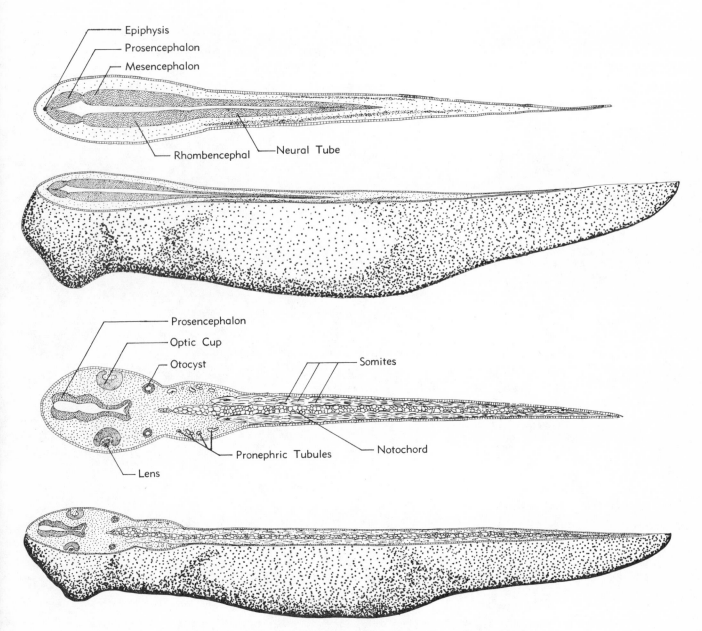

Figure 9. Six Millimeter Frog Embryo Frontal Sections.

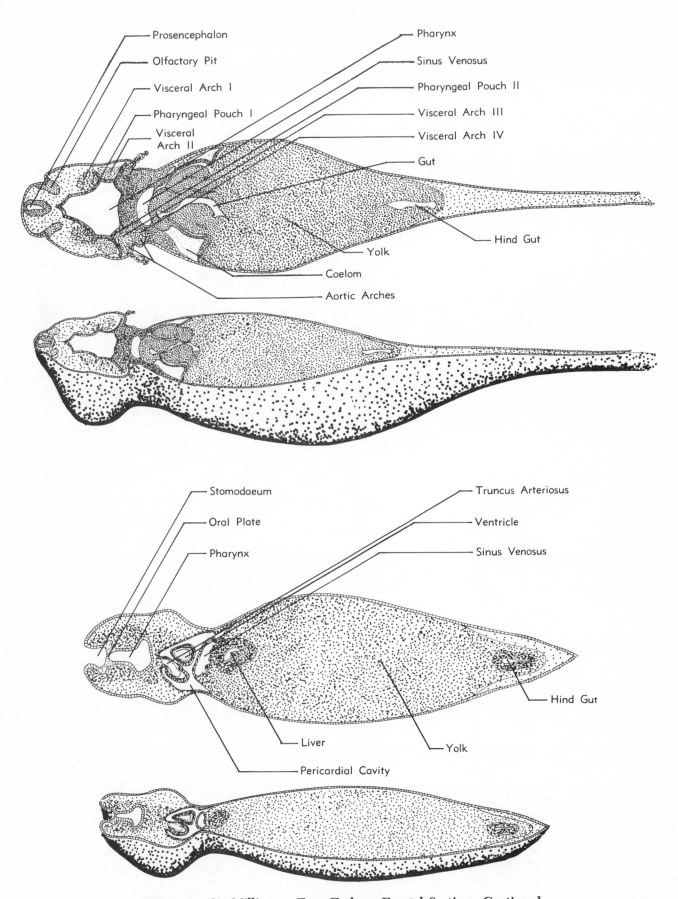

Figure 9. Six Millimeter Frog Embryo Frontal Sections, Continued.

The Eight Millimeter Frog Embryo Sagittal Sections

Material

A serial sagittal section of the 8 mm frog embryo.

Discussion

Between 6 mm and 8 mm considerable development occurs. The tail has become more prominent and the body more compact. The embryo has hatched and is swimming about but is still living on the yolk. The *oral plate* is about to rupture so feeding can begin.

The brain has developed, and the five brain vesicles can be distinguished. The prosencephalon has divided into the *telencephalon* and the *diencephalon*. The *mesencephalon* remains undivided, but the rhombencephalon has divided into the *metencephalon* and the *myelencephalon*. The relatively large *infundibulum* is beginning to be constricted between the *optic chiasma* and the *posterior tubercle*. Further development of the sense organs will be described for the 10 mm embryo.

Most of the development of the digestive tract is occurring in the pharyngeal region. The external gills are well developed and are exchanging gases with the surrounding water. The gill slits begin opening at this stage, and the mouth begins to operate as a pump, causing water to flow over the gills to aid in respiration. Five pairs of visceral pouches and six pairs of visceral arches should be present. The midgut has begun to elongate and coil, forming the intestine. The liver tissue is beginning to proliferate. It is intimately associated with the vitelline veins.

The circulatory system is continuing its development. As additional visceral arches differentiate, they are each supplied with an aortic arch. The ventral aortae continue cephalad of the aortic arches as the external carotid arteries. Also, anterior projections of the paired dorsal aortae form the internal carotid arteries. Most of the changes in the circulatory system are a matter of growth and rapid extensions of the circulatory network.

The pronephric tubules form in the region of somites 2, 3 and 4. One end opens into the coelom by a ciliated opening called the *nephrostome*. The other end opens into the pronephric duct. The tubules are much coiled in the 8 mm embryo and in the sections they are cut several times. Opposite each nephrostome small protuberances extend out from the aorta. These are called *glomi* (singular, glomus).

Exercise

Place your 8 mm serial sagittal section on your microscope and study the sections from side to side. Work to integrate the sections into a three-dimensional picture and keep at it until you can do this. Remember to master your slide before doing any drawing.

Drawings

Choose the section of your serial that comes the nearest to being a median sagittal section and draw it in the middle of a sheet of drawing paper. Then draw the sections on either side, one at the top of the sheet and the other at the bottom.

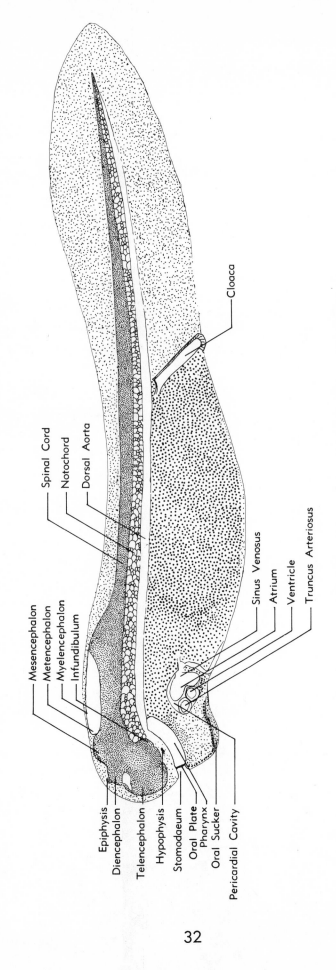

Cloaca

Spinal Cord
Notochord
Dorsal Aorta

Mesencephalon
Metencephalon
Myelencephalon
Infundibulum

Sinus Venosus
Atrium
Ventricle
Truncus Arteriosus

Epiphysis
Diencephalon
Telencephalon
Hypophysis
Stomodaeum
Oral Plate
Pharynx
Oral Sucker
Pericardial Cavity

Figure 10. Eight Millimeter Frog Embryo Median Sagittal Section.

32

Labels

Label the following structures on your drawings:

Atrium	Optic Chiasma
Cloaca	Optic Recess
Diencephalon	Oral Plate
Dorsal Aorta	Oral Sucker
Epiphysis	Pericardial Cavity
Hypophysis	Posterior Tubercle
Infundibulum	Sinus Venosus
Mesencephalon	Stomodaeum
Metencephalon	Telencephalon
Myelencephalon	Truncus Arteriosus
Notochord	Ventricle

Questions

1. What changes have occurred in the brain between 6 mm and 8 mm?
2. What is the source of food for the 6 to 8 mm larva?
3. When does the oral plate disappear?
4. When do the gill clefts open?
5. Why are the larva's first gills external?
6. What mechanism is essential to the functioning of internal gills?
7. Where are the aortic arches always located?
8. What change occurs in the infundibulum between 6 mm and 8 mm?
9. Describe the pronephros of the frog.
10. Does the pronephros function as an excretory organ in the frog? Look up the arguments pro and con.

EXERCISE XII

The Eight Millimeter Frog Embryo
Serial Cross Sections

Material

A serial cross section of an 8 mm frog embryo.

Discussion

Read again the discussion of Exercise XI.

Exercise

Place the slide on your microscope and beginning with the sections at the anterior end of the embryo, study them section by section until you can recognize all the structures. After you have done this, go through the sections again and try to integrate what you see into a three-dimensional picture. Persist in this until you have success.

Drawings

After you have mastered your serial, choose a series of sections for drawing. The choice is up to you, but be sure you include all structures and structural patterns.

Labels

Label the following structures on your drawings:

Afferent Branchial Artery	Dorsal Aorta
Auditory Vesicle	Foregut
Diencephalon	Ganglia VII & VIII
	Ganglion V

Gut	Pronephric Duct
Hypophysis	Pronephric Tubule
Infundibulum	Rhombencephalon
Lens	Somite
Liver	Stomodaeum
Mesencephalon	Telencephalon
Notochord	Thyroid
Olfactory Pit	Truncus Arteriosus
Optic Cup	Ventricle
Oral Sucker	Yolk

Questions

1. How is the shape of the embryo changing at 8 mm?
2. How many pairs of visceral pouches appear during frog development?
3. What develops from the first visceral pouch?
4. Which of the visceral pouches develop into gill slits?
5. How many visceral arches appear during frog development?
6. On which of the visceral arches are the external gills found?
7. From which of the visceral arches do the internal gills develop?
8. Which of the visceral pouches become gill clefts?
9. Describe a pronephric tubule.
10. From what embryonic blood vessels do the internal carotid arteries develop?

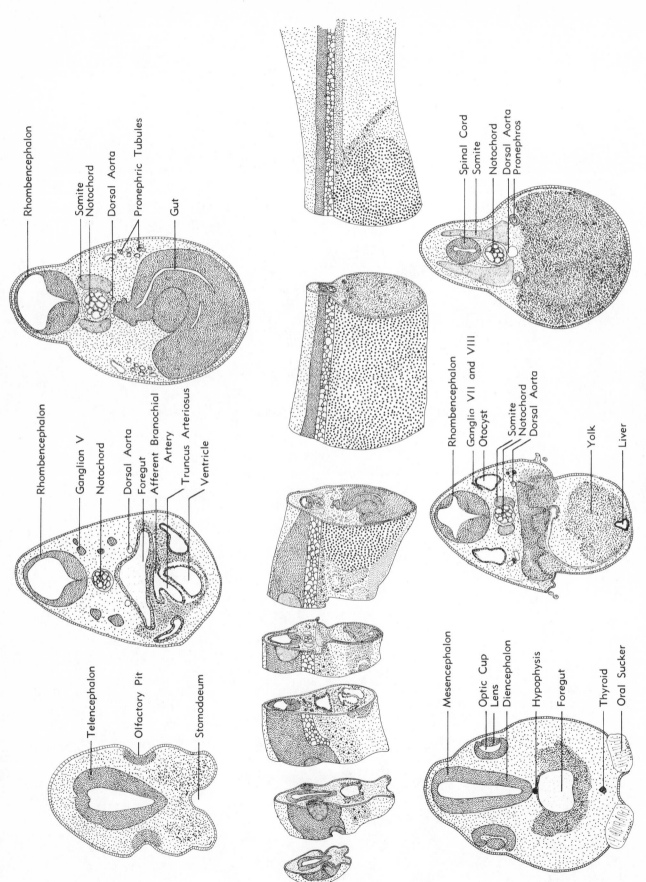

Figure 11. Eight Millimeter Frog Embryo Sectioned.

Rhombencephalon
Somite
Notochord
Dorsal Aorta
Pronephric Tubules
Gut

Spinal Cord
Somite
Notochord
Dorsal Aorta
Pronephros

Rhombencephalon
Ganglion V
Notochord
Dorsal Aorta
Foregut
Afferent Branchial Artery
Truncus Arteriosus
Ventricle

Rhombencephalon
Ganglia VII and VIII
Otocyst
Somite
Notochord
Dorsal Aorta
Yolk
Liver

Telencephalon
Olfactory Pit
Stomodaeum

Mesencephalon
Optic Cup
Lens
Diencephalon
Hypophysis
Foregut
Thyroid
Oral Sucker

35

EXERCISE XIII

The Ten Millimeter Frog Embryo
Serial Sagittal Sections

Material

A serial sagittal section of a 10 mm frog embryo.

Discussion

At 10 mm the frog larva has assumed the typical tadpole shape. It consists of an oval body which has been flattened dorso-ventrally and a large tail for swimming. The external gills have been largely, if not entirely, covered by the *operculum* which has grown caudad from the second visceral arch. The operculum begins as two folds of skin starting from the two members of the second pair of visceral arches. These skin folds first grow caudad and later ventrad, fusing in the midventral line to form the *opercular* or *peribranchial chamber*. The thin posterior borders of these skin folds fuse with the skin to form a closed chamber except for a small pore called the *spiracle* on the left side. Water is taken into the mouth, passes over the gills into the peribranchial chamber and out through the spiracle. After being covered by the operculum, the external gills atrophy and are replaced by a new set called the *internal gills*.

The telencephalon is beginning to be divided into two lateral lobes, the *lateral telencephalic vesicles*. The structure separating them is called the *lamina terminalis*. The olfactory pits have opened into the mouth cavity, forming the *internal nares* and have made contact with the telencephalon, forming the *olfactory tract*.

On the ventral side of the diencephalon are two evaginations. They are the *optic recess* and the *infundibulum*. The latter will join the hypophysis to form the *pituitary* gland. Between them is an elevation, the *optic chiasma*. The sides of the diencephalon thicken to form the *optic thalami*. The epiphysis is, of course, on the dorsal side of the diencephalon. The eyes, which connect to the diencephalon by means of the optic nerves, are well developed in the 10 mm larva. The *retina* has divided into an outer *pigmented layer* and an inner *sensory layer*; and the sensory layer has, in turn, differentiated into *rods* and *cones*, *ganglionic layer* and so forth. The *vitreous body* has formed, and the eyes are near completion.

The walls of the mesencephalon thicken, reducing the mesocoel to the narrow *aqueduct of Sylvius*. A pair of enlargements on the dorsal sides becomes the *optic lobes*.

The auditory vesicle has been divided by an oblique septum into an upper *utriculus* and a lower *sacculus*. Later the *semicircular canals* will form from the utriculus and then largely separate from it, and the sacculus will produce a lateral evagination called the *lagena*. In higher vertebrates the lagena develops into the *cochlea*. The *middle ear* and the *eustachian tube* develop from the first visceral pouch.

The visceral pouches and visceral arches have been adequately described in preceding exercises, and the development of the gills has also been described. A diverticulum forms ventrally on the posterior portion of the pharynx. This grows out and bifurcates and develops into the *glottis*, *trachea*, *bronchi* and *lungs*. Behind the glottis, the foregut differentiates into the *esophagus* and the *stomach*. Behind the stomach is the liver diver-

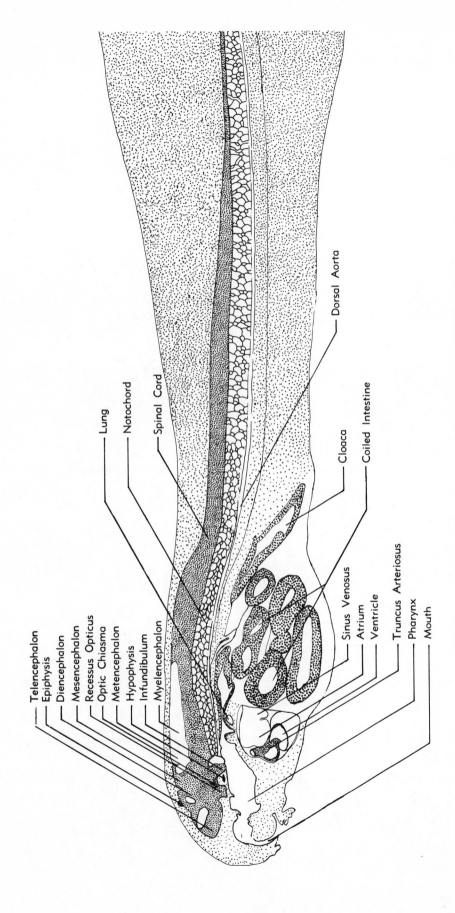

Telencephalon
Epiphysis
Diencephalon
Mesencephalon
Recessus Opticus
Optic Chiasma
Metencephalon
Hypophysis
Infundibulum
Myelencephalon

Lung
Notochord
Spinal Cord

Dorsal Aorta

Cloaca
Coiled Intestine

Sinus Venosus
Atrium
Ventricle
Truncus Arteriosus
Pharynx
Mouth

Figure 12.   Ten Millimeter Frog Embryo Median Sagittal Section.

ticulum which has been previously described. The midgut elongates and twists upon itself, forming the long *intestine*. The *cloaca* forms from the hindgut and the proctodaeum. The *urinary bladder* develops from the entodermal portion of the cloaca.

The two vitelline veins enter the sinus venosus. At first they are about the same size, but with the growth of the liver the left one increases in size and the right one begins to atrophy. It finally disappears entirely. The left vitelline vein breaks into multiple passageways through the liver. That portion of the left vitelline vein between the liver and the sinus venosus becomes the *hepatic vein*, and that portion posterior to the liver becomes the *hepatic portal vein*.

The posterior cardinal veins largely disappear and are replaced by a vein of complex origin called the *posterior vena cava*. The two ducts of Cuvier fuse to form the *anterior vena cava*, and the anterior cardinal veins become the *jugular veins*. Much of the development of the circulatory system, including some of that already described, lies beyond the scope of this manual.

The two pronephroi have become rather conspicuous. They lie lateral to the notochord. At a later time they will atrophy and be replaced by the *mesonephroi*. The development of the reproductive system begins with the development of two *genital ridges* on either side and ventral to the notochord. Further development comes later.

Exercise

The procedures for studying the various kinds of sections should be familiar to you by now. If in doubt, turn back to preceding exercises and review. Put the 10 mm serial sagittal section slides on the microscope and study thoroughly.

Drawings

Make three drawings of this series, choosing them as you did in the case of the 8 mm sagittals.

Labels

Label the following structures on your drawings:

Atrium	Mouth
Cloaca	Myelencephalon
Coiled Intestine	Notochord
Diencephalon	Optic Chiasma
Dorsal Aorta	Optic Recess
Epiphysis	Pharynx
Hypophysis	Sinus Venosus
Infundibulum	Spinal Cord
Lung Buds	Telencephalon
Mesencephalon	Truncus Arteriosus
Metencephalon	Ventricle

Questions

1. Discuss the origin and fate of the external gills.
2. Describe the operculum, its origin, source and growth.
3. Describe respiration in the frog larva.
4. What changes occur in the olfactory pits at about the 10 mm stage?
5. With what part of the brain do the olfactory pits make contact?
6. How are the internal nares formed?
7. Discuss the embryology of the pituitary gland.
8. What names are given to the cavities inside the five brain vesicles?
9. Identify the four ventricles of adult brain anatomy with the cavities in the five vesicles of the embryonic brain.
10. What is the fate of the mesocoel?

The Ten Millimeter Frog Embryo
Serial Cross Sections

Material

A serial cross section of a 10 mm frog embryo.

Discussion

By the time the frog embryo has reached the length of 10 mm it has become a complex organism. It is hoped the student will accept the challenge both of mastering the structure of this embryo and of tracing the development of each organ and system from its beginning to its present state of development. Read again the discussion in Exercise XIII.

Exercise

Study the serial cross section of the 10 mm embryo, using the same procedures and techniques you have used in the study of previous cross sections. Remember the importance of visualizing the embryo and its parts in three dimensions. This embryo will be more difficult, but persistence and thoroughness will pay big dividends.

Drawings

Make a series of cross-sectional drawings that will include all the structures of this embryo with their variations. Use the criteria you have learned in previous exercises for deciding which sections to draw. Make your drawings neat, accurate and proportional. Locate each of your sections on your median sagittal section by a suitably labeled line drawn across it.

Labels

Label the following structures on your drawings:

Afferent Branchial Artery	Mouth
Auditory Nerve	Muscle
Auditory Vesicle	Myelencephalon
Branchial Pouch	Notochord
Cartilages	Olfactory Epithelium
Cloaca	Opercular Cavity
Coiled Intestine	Optic Cup
Diencephalon	Oral Sucker
Dorsal Aorta	Parachordal Cartilage
Dorsal Fin	Pharynx
Esophagus	Prechordal Cartilage
Foregut	Pronephros
Internal Gills	Sinus Venosus
Lens	Spinal Cord
Lung Buds	Telencephalon
Mesenchyme	Truncus Arteriosus

Questions

1. Describe the changes that have occurred in the telencephalon since the 8 mm stage.
2. Describe the differentiation of the retina.
3. What structures develop on the dorsal side of the mesencephalon?
4. Describe the origin of the lungs, trachea and so forth.
5. From which of the three regions of the embryonic gut are the esophagus and stomach derived?

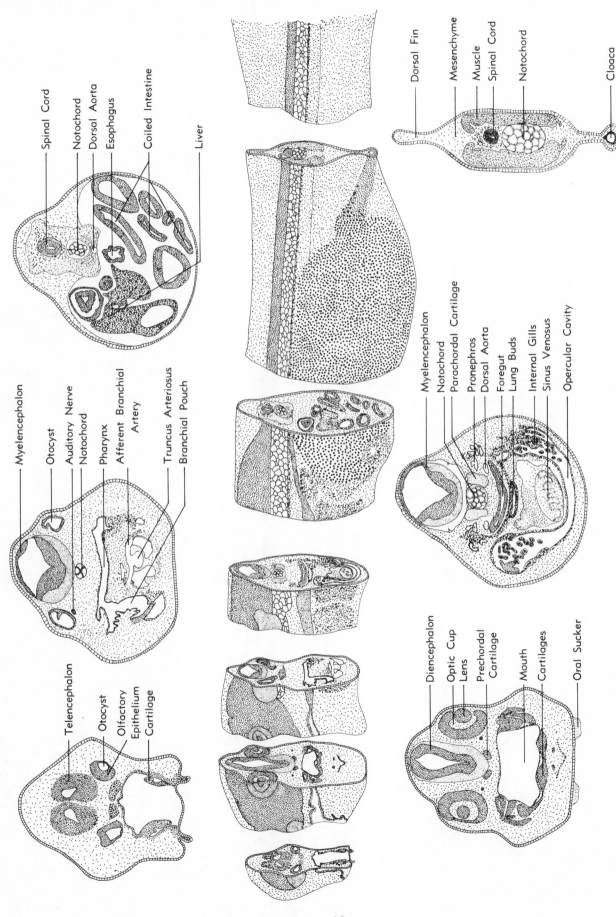

Figure 13. Ten Millimeter Frog Embryo Sectioned.

6. Locate the attachment of the liver diverticulum to the gut.
7. What changes occur in the midgut between the 8 mm and the 10 mm stages?
8. Give the embryonic source of the urinary bladder.
9. Describe the development of the hepatic portal system.
10. Describe the development of the renal portal system.

EXERCISE XV

The Ten Millimeter Frog Embryo
Frontal Sections

Material

A serial frontal section of a 10 mm frog embryo.

Discussion

Read again the discussion of the 10 mm embryo that is found in Exercise XIII. Consult your text and other sources to get a complete picture of the anatomy of this embryo.

Exercise

Up to this point an attempt has been made to give you adequate visual aids to guide you in your study of the whole mounts and the various kinds of sections; however, this manual contains no 10 mm frontal sections, and you may have trouble finding suitable illustrations in other books. This will give you the opportunity to try out the skills you have been learning.

Place the 10 mm frontal section slides on your microscope and study through the sections. Identify all the organs and systems you can. By comparing these sections with the cross and sagittal sections work out the identification of all structures you do not recognize or you are uncertain about. Having finished this, work on your three-dimensional image of the 10 mm embryo, using all your slides and all the visual aids available.

Drawings

Make a series of frontal section drawings that will adequately cover the structure and relationships of the various organs and systems.

Labels

Adequately label your drawings.

Questions

1. Describe the differentiation of the auditory vesicles.
2. Give the origin of the semicircular canals.
3. What is the function of the semicircular canals?
4. With what structure in higher vertebrates is the lagena homologous?
5. Explain the fate of the posterior cardinal veins.
6. Explain the relationship between the posterior vena cava and the developing liver.
7. Describe the processes that lead to the formation of the anterior vena cava.
8. What adult blood vessels develop from the anterior cardinal veins?
9. Describe the pronephros of the 10 mm frog embryo.
10. What structure found in the 10 mm embryo is the beginning of the reproductive system?